Bible Heroes: Joshua, Gid and Ruth

by Dee Leone

illustrated by Veronica Terrill

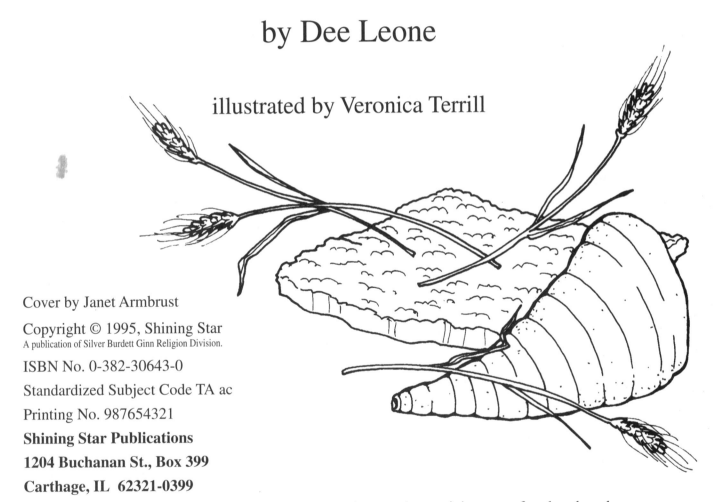

Cover by Janet Armbrust

Copyright © 1995, Shining Star
A publication of Silver Burdett Ginn Religion Division.

ISBN No. 0-382-30643-0

Standardized Subject Code TA ac

Printing No. 987654321

Shining Star Publications

1204 Buchanan St., Box 399

Carthage, IL 62321-0399

Unless otherwise indicated, the New International Version of the Bible was used in preparing the activities in this book.

To the Teacher/Parent

Bible Heroes: Joshua, Gideon, and Ruth is filled with Bible story coloring pages, activity puzzles, patterns, games, songs, and plays designed to make your study of these three Bible characters a real celebration!

The first page of each unit contains a simplified story to introduce your children to the Bible hero. The next page of each unit has suggestions and reproducible patterns designed to get your celebration off to a good start. The coloring book pages that follow reinforce story concepts and help children to visualize biblical scenes.

Each coloring book page has a corresponding activity page to go with it. "A New Leader," the first coloring book page, for example, goes along with "Going to Jericho," the first activity page. Each day you may want to have the children complete a coloring page and the corresponding activity page. After all the coloring pages of a unit have been discussed and completed, they may be made into keepsake story booklets.

The patterns included with each unit may be used to create puppets and other visual aids designed to make the story, songs, and plays come alive. The patterns can be backed with felt for use on a flannel board, or they can be attached to ice-cream sticks for use with a box stage. Enlarged patterns may be made into paper bag puppets or stick masks. They may also be used to create bulletin boards, mobiles, murals, props, and backdrops.

The delightful song lyrics in this book help to emphasize play parts and story parts. The words may be sung to familiar, catchy tunes. In addition, games and crafts are included to reinforce Bible story concepts.

A number of exciting activities can be used to end each unit. For example, children can display their crafts on a table and invite others to their Bible hero "museum." Another fun way to end the units would be to play the games and use related objects as prizes. These might include Bible stickers, buttons, bookmarks, stationery, or pencil toppers made from the Bible patterns given in this book. Of course, one of the best ways to culminate each unit would be with a performance of the plays and songs—a sure way to delight audiences of all ages!

Dedication

To Corina and Nicole

0-382-30643-0

Table of Contents

Joshua

Gideon

Ruth

Shining Star, Copyright © 1995

0-382-30643-0

The Story of Joshua

A Story Based on Joshua 1, 2, 3, 4, and 6

(Note: Use some of the patterns on pages 5, 15-17, 35, and 55 to create flannel board pieces, stick puppets, or play props to emphasize the underlined words of the story.)

After Moses died, the Lord put Joshua in charge of the Israelites. He told Joshua to get the people ready to cross the Jordon to enter the promised land. While the people were getting ready, Joshua sent two spies to look over the land. The spies went to Jericho and stayed at the house of a woman named Rahab. The king of Jericho found out and sent some of his men to Rahab's house. Rahab told the king's men that she didn't know the men were spies. She also told them that the men had left, even though she had really hidden the men on her roof under some stacks of flax.

The king's men hurried off hoping to find the spies. Then Rahab went to the spies and said, "I know the Lord will soon give this land to the Israelites. Everyone is afraid because we have heard how the Lord parted the sea for you when you left Egypt. Since I have kept you safe, promise me that you will keep me and my family safe when you take over this land." The spies climbed out Rahab's window and told her to hang a red cord in the window as a sign to the Israelites not to harm those inside. Then they hid in the hills for three days while the king's men searched for them along the road. When they returned to camp, they told Joshua that the Lord would surely give them the land, for the people of Jericho were so afraid of them.

At the Jordan, Joshua told the priests to take up the ark. When the priests carrying the ark set foot in the river, the water stopped flowing and piled up in a heap. Then all the Israelites crossed the Jordan on dry ground. Joshua had one man from each tribe take a stone from the Jordan. Then he told the priests to step out of the Jordan. Immediately, the water flowed back into place. The twelve stones, one for each tribe, were set near the border of Jericho to forever serve as a sign of what the Lord had done.

Once the Israelites crossed the Jordan, the people of Jericho kept their city tightly shut. No one went out and no one went in. The Lord spoke to Joshua and said, "March around the city with your people once a day for six days. Have seven priests carry trumpets of rams' horns in front of the ark. On the seventh day, march around the city seven times. When the priests sound a long trumpet blast, have the people give a loud shout. The walls of Jericho will fall down, and you and your men will be able to go straight into the city."

Joshua called the priests and people together and they began to march. First, came the armed guard, then the seven priests with trumpets, then the ark, and finally, the rear guard. They all marched around Jericho once a day for six days.

On the seventh day, they marched around the city seven times. The seventh time around, when the priests gave a long blast on their trumpets, Joshua ordered the people to shout. The people shouted and the walls of Jericho fell down. Joshua's army marched straight in and took the city. Only Rahab and her family were saved, because Rahab had treated the spies kindly.

And so, the Lord was with Joshua and he became famous throughout the land.

Shining Star, Copyright © 1995

0-382-30643-0

Celebrating the Bible Hero, Joshua

Join in the Joshua Fun

1. Write the verses (such as Joshua 6:16) on the trumpets for children to memorize. Display them on a bulletin board entitled "Make a Joyful Noise to the Lord." Copy a Jericho certificate (above) for each child. Each time a child memorizes a verse, write the verse number on his certificate.

2. Have children start a Joshua Journal of creative writing assignments. These might include a "No More Manna" menu, a research project entitled "Joshua's Journeys," poems or songs for a page entitled "Joshua Jingles," a coded "Joshua Jumble" letter to Joshua from one of the spies, and even some Joshua jokes.

3. Use the trumpet as a pencil topper for a job well done; add it to the top of a heavy strip of paper to create a Bible bookmark, or use it as a prize for winning a Joshua game.

4. Have children create rules and supplies for a game entitled "Knocking Down Jericho," "Hide the Spy," or "Seven Priests and Seven Trumpets." Possible prizes might include Joshua Jigsaw puzzles made from the coloring pages in this book.

5. Use the certificate above as an invitation to a play or Joshua Jamboree, as an award for a great performance, as a reward for completion of the Joshua coloring booklet, as a take-home memory verse card, or as a thank-you note.

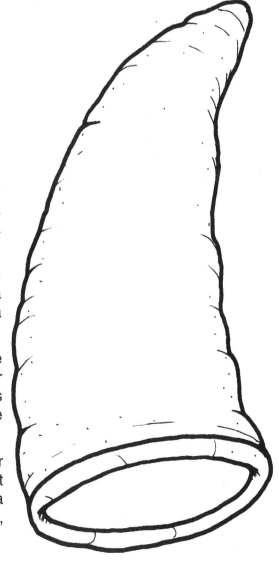

5

0-382-30643-0

Spies in Jericho

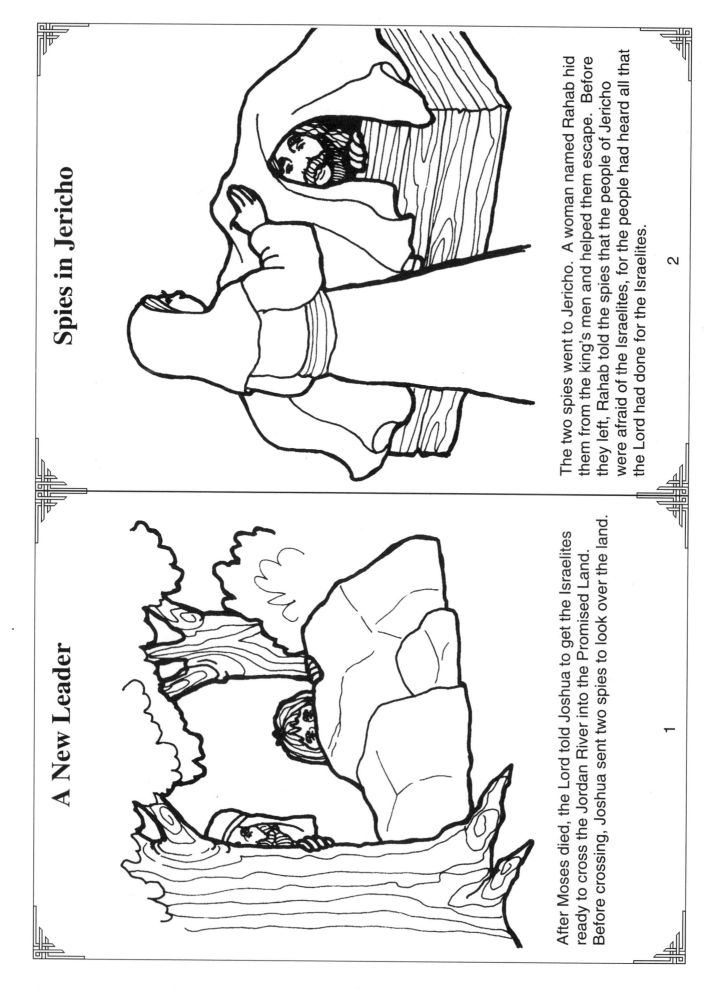

The two spies went to Jericho. A woman named Rahab hid them from the king's men and helped them escape. Before they left, Rahab told the spies that the people of Jericho were afraid of the Israelites, for the people had heard all that the Lord had done for the Israelites.

2

A New Leader

After Moses died, the Lord told Joshua to get the Israelites ready to cross the Jordan River into the Promised Land. Before crossing, Joshua sent two spies to look over the land.

1

0-382-30643-0

Seven Priests

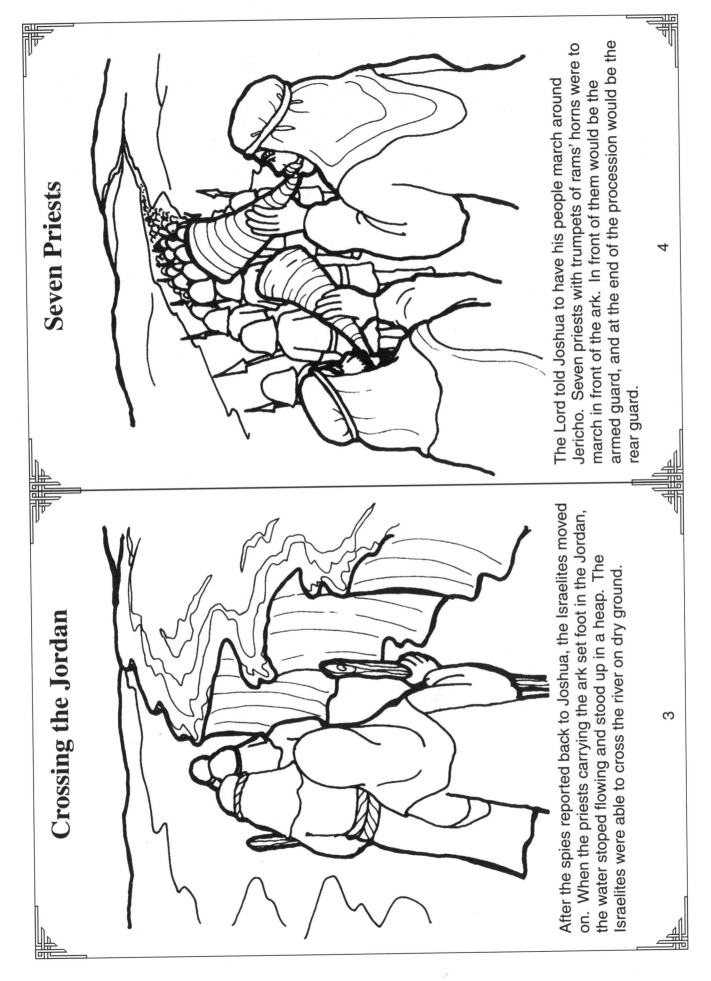

The Lord told Joshua to have his people march around Jericho. Seven priests with trumpets of rams' horns were to march in front of the ark. In front of them would be the armed guard, and at the end of the procession would be the rear guard.

4

Crossing the Jordan

After the spies reported back to Joshua, the Israelites moved on. When the priests carrying the ark set foot in the Jordan, the water stoped flowing and stood up in a heap. The Israelites were able to cross the river on dry ground.

3

0-382-30643-0

The Walls Fall Down

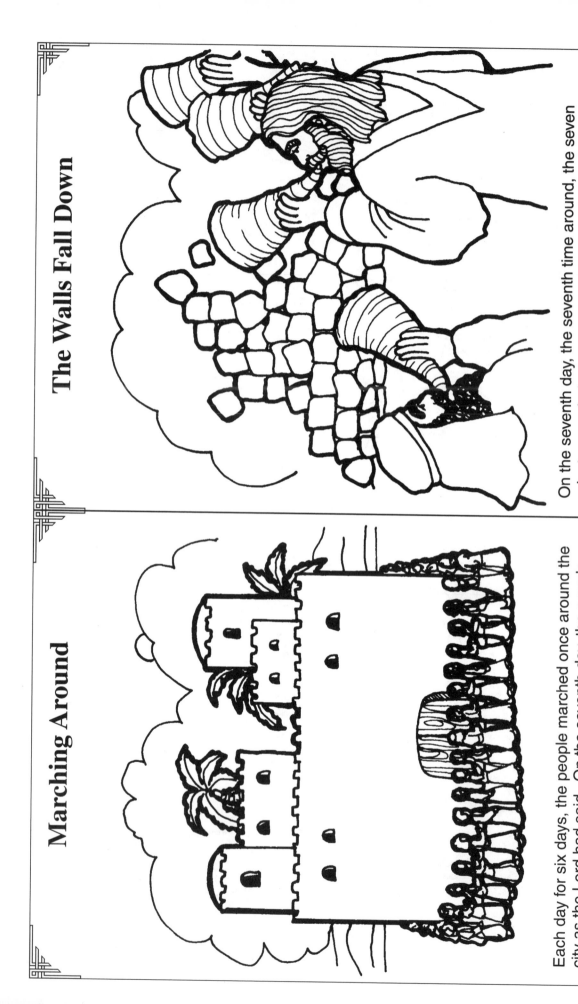

On the seventh day, the seventh time around, the seven priests sounded a long trumpet blast. The people shouted and the walls of Jericho tumbled down. Then the people marched in and took the city. Only Rahab and her family were saved because Rahab had been kind to the spies.

6

Marching Around

Each day for six days, the people marched once around the city as the Lord had said. On the seventh day, the people marched around the city seven times.

5

0-382-30643-0

Going to Jericho

Help the spies find the shortest path to Jericho. Then write the letters from the path in order on the blanks to complete the Bible verse.

T	H	E	R	E	O	N	O	D	T	O	G	O	T	O
H	E	N	E	S	S	A	F	A	H	C	E	R	E	J
E	N	J	I	U	A	N	N	H	O	H	O	V	E	R
N	I	O	S	H	G	D	U	N	W	O	K	E	N	T
J	T	W	A	S	O	C	E	S	I	F	O	R	M	H
O	H	A	P	P	D	R	A	H	T	L	O	T	I	E
S	O	N	E	Y	I	E	V	R	T	O	E	H	L	H
E	T	T	S	Y	L	T	S	E	M	G	L	E	K	O
P	W	N	A	W	J	G	M	E	I	P	P	L	T	N
H	O	A	D	R	O	N	I	T	T	A	N	A	O	E
A	S	P	O	I	L	S	H	I	N	Y	D	L	Y	J
N	D	I	R	O	O	M	A	N	D	E	H	L	R	E
O	M	E	S	F	R	O	L	I	A	S	E	A	I	C
S	E	S	M	E	O	Z	E	D	T	O	C	I	T	H	O
F	E	L	O	H	M	T	H	E	S	P	E	C	S	O

"___ ___ ___ ___ ___ ___ ___ ___ ___ ___

___ ___ ___ ___ ___ ___ ___ ___

___ ___ ___ ___ ___ ___ ___ ___ ___ ___

___ ___ ___ ___ ___ . '___ ___, ___ ___ ___ ___

___ ___ ___ ___, ___ ___ ___ ___,

'___ ___ ___ ___ ___ ___ ___ ___ ___ ___ ___.'"

Joshua 2:1

9

0-382-30643-0

Spies in Hiding

There are spies hiding in each set of letters. Cross out the word *SPIES* in each set of letters.
The remaining letters will spell a word. Write each word on the correct lines at the bottom of
the page to find out what Rahab did with the spies.

1. SPIBEUTS
2. HASPIDES
3. TSHPIEESM
4. STOPIES
5. ROSPOIFES
6. HSPIIDDEENS

7. SSPTAILEKSS
8. SPIFLEAXS
9. OSUPITES
10. SSHPIEES
11. STAPIKEENS
12. SUPPIES

13. THSPIESE
14. ASPINEDS
15. SPUNIDEERS
16. SOPIFES
17. SLAPIIEDS
18. SONPIES

"(_____ _____ _____ _____
　　1　　　　　10　　　　　2　　　　　11

_____ _____ _____ _____
　　3　　　　　12　　　　　4　　　　　13

_____ _____ _____ _____
　　5　　　　　14　　　　　6　　　　　3

_____ _____ _____ _____
　　15　　　　　13　　　　　7　　　　　16

_____ _____ _____ _____
　　8　　　　　10　　　　　2　　　　　17

_____ _____ _____ _____.)"
　　9　　　　　18　　　　　13　　　　　5

Joshua 2:6

0-382-30643-0

On Dry Ground

Find and circle ten things that are different in the bottom picture.

"The priests who carried the ark of the covenant of the Lord stood firm on dry ground in the middle of the Jordan, while all Israel passed by until the whole nation had completed the crossing on dry ground."

Joshua 3:17

11

0-382-30643-0

Seven Priests with Seven Trumpets

Find and circle the word *PRIEST* and the word *TRUMPET* seven times in the puzzle below.

```
B   E   M   I   T   F   T   G   T   S   E   I   R   P   K
T   P   J   D   N   P   R   I   E   S   T   F   D   C   G
I   L   R   T   A   J   U   Y   D   C   W   T   A   L   T
M   H   K   I   F   Y   M   A   A   L   S   Y   Y   R   R
E   T   I   M   E   J   P   D   Y   E   A   J   U   N   U
P   K   F   E   G   S   E   N   I   D   E   M   I   T   M
T   R   U   M   P   E   T   R   U   M   P   E   T   H   P
G   H   I   C   D   B   P   R   I   E   S   T   W   J   E
T   I   M   E   N   A   K   F   T   R   U   M   P   E   T
Y   A   D   L   S   H   T   T   E   P   M   U   R   T   G
C   K   E   M   I   T   J   P   R   I   E   S   T   B   H
```

"Have seven priests carry trumpets of rams' horns in front of the ark. On the seventh day, march around the city seven times, with the priests blowing the trumpets."

Joshua 6:4

0-382-30643-0

Seven Times Around

Circle around the city clockwise seven times, writing every seventh letter in order on the blanks. When done correctly, you will spell out a Bible verse.

Start here

T S H M E S U H G O A T S N E I U N B O D S V T D L

Left column (top to bottom): T O T P M S A Y R S M O E H T A E U C L D I E I R A P R C M R T U

Right column (top to bottom): L U W E E F E A N H V N O D S D E E Y R T T E N N O T H J D T T U

Bottom row: U O O E I P E H E L H T E H S P E T H H T O E H U

"T H ___ ___ ___ ___ ___ ___ ___

___ ___ ___ ___ ___ ___, ___ ___ ___ ___ ___

___ ___ ___ ___ ___ ___ ___ ___ ___

___ ___ ___ ___ ___ ___

___ ___ ___ ___ ___ , ___ ___ ___ ___

___ ___ ___ ___ ___ ___ ___ ___ ___

___ ___ ___ ___ ___, ' ___ ___ ___ ___ ___ !

___ ___ ___ ___ ___ ___ ___ ___

___ ___ ___ ___ ___ ___ ___ ___ ___ ___ ___

___ ___ ___ ___ ___ !'"

Joshua 6:16

0-382-30643-0

Tumbled Wall Jumble

Unscramble each set of letters. Then use the words to complete the verse below.

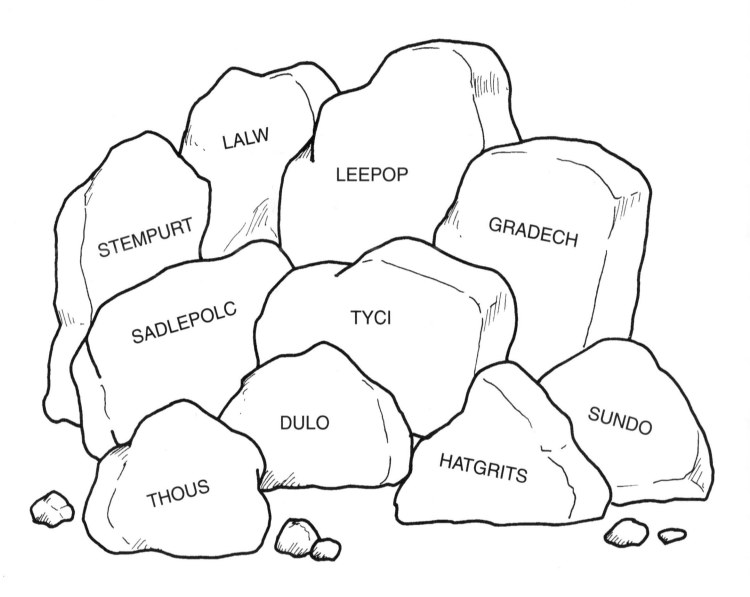

"When the ___ ___ ___ ___ ___ ___ ___ ___ sounded, the ___ ___ ___ ___ ___ ___

shouted, and at the ___ ___ ___ ___ ___ of the trumpet, when the people gave a

___ ___ ___ ___ ___ ___ ___ ___ ___, the ___ ___ ___ ___

___ ___ ___ ___ ___ ___ ___ ___ ___; so every man ___ ___ ___ ___ ___ ___ ___

___ ___ ___ ___ ___ ___ ___ in, and they took the ___ ___ ___ ___."

Joshua 6:20

Shining Star, Copyright © 1995

0-382-30643-0

Joshua/Boaz Mask

Color, cut out, and laminate this mask. To make a face mask, punch a small hole on each side and add string or elastic. To make a stick mask, glue a paint stirring stick to the back. To make a puppet, attach this face to a paper bag. Use it when putting on a presentation about Joshua. (This pattern may also represent Boaz in the story of Ruth later in this book.)

0-382-30643-0

Joshua Finger Puppet and Song

Color and cut out the figures below and on page 17. Glue each one to a ring-sized paper band. Use them as you perform the song. You may want to laminate the figures or back them with lightweight cardboard before cutting them out. Then glue an ice-cream stick to the back of each one to make a stick puppet to use with a shoe box stage or back the figures with felt for use with a flannel board. The figures may also be enlarged to make stick puppets.

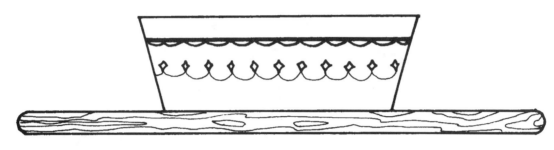

ARK

JOSHUA

SOLDIER

Marching Israelites
Tune: "Yankee Doodle"

I'm the leader, Joshua.
It's under my command
That we will take possession of
The fruitful promised land.

Chorus:
Marching Israelites are we.
Around and round we go.
Marching, marching all around
The walls of Jericho.

I'm a guard in Joshua's army,
I am strong and fit-ee.
I march before the seven priests
Around the walled-up city.

I'm a priest. I'm one of seven
With a horn to blow.
We march before the sacred ark.
We're lined up in a row.

The ark of the Lord's covenant
Is next in the procession.
It is a sacred object in
The Israelites' possession.

I'm a soldier in the army.
My job is just fine.
I'm a part of the rear guard…
Which means I'm last in line.

GUARD

PRIEST

0-382-30643-0

Joshua Bible Story Patterns

Reduce or enlarge these figures and the ones on page 16. Use them for puppets, flannel board stories, bulletin board displays, shoe box dioramas, shoe box stages, stationery, pencil toppers, storytelling, play props or backgrounds.

SPY

JORDAN

HILLS/LAND

JERICHO/CITY

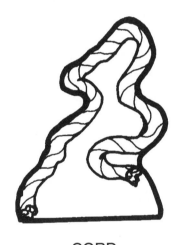

CORD

KING'S MEN

RAHAB

STONE

Shining Star, Copyright © 1995

0-382-30643-0

Somewhere Over the River
Dreaming of the Promised Land

Characters: Joshua, Tyler, Dad, Spy 1, Spy 2, Narrator, Chorus, 7 Priests, Israelites/Army Men

Setting: The Israelite camp is at stage left, and a paper river is at center stage and should extend toward the front of the stage or possibly outside the stage curtain, if there is one.

Props: Cardboard box wall that includes a window opening with red cord hanging out, tent and other campsite items, paper river, 7 trumpets, box to serve as the ark, backpack with robe inside, beard

Tyler: *(Joshua and Tyler dressed in school clothes enter and go to the front of stage or front of curtain where the river is sticking out.)* That sure was a neat Bible story the teacher read to us today.

Joshua: Yes, especially since the hero, Joshua, had the same name as me.

Tyler: Look, a big puddle! Let's pretend it's the River Jordan.

Joshua: I'm Joshua. Here I go across the river! *(He jumps up, slips, hits his head, and lies still.)*

Tyler: Joshua, Joshua! Wake up! Are you all right? *(Joshua lies still. Tyler opens backpack, takes out robe, and covers Joshua.)* That'll keep him warm while I get help. *(Tyler runs off. Curtain opens to reveal spies waking up Joshua. If there's no curtain, spies simply walk on stage.)*

Spy 1: Joshua, Joshua! Wake up! We've come to tell you about Jericho. *(Joshua adds beard and gets up as he wraps the robe around him to signify that he is now Joshua, the Israelite, not the schoolboy.)*

Spy 2: The Lord will surely give us the city, for the people there are in fear of us.

Joshua: Tell me everything.

Spy 1: We went to Jericho and stayed at the house of a woman named Rahab, but someone figured out that we were spies and told the king. Soon the king's men came to Rahab's house and started asking questions.

Chorus: *(Sing "Are the Spies Still Here?" page 20)*

Spy 2: Rahab told them we had left, but really she had hidden us on her roof. When the king's men left, Rahab let us out her window with a rope.

Chorus: *(Sing "Rahab let the Spies Climb Down," page 20)*

Spy 1: Before Rahab helped us escape, she told us that all of Jericho was afraid of us, for they knew the Lord helped us cross the sea on dry ground.

Spy 2: Because she saved our lives, we promised not to harm anyone in her house when we take the city. A red cord will be in her window.

0-382-30643-0

Narrator: After hearing the spies' report, Joshua and the Israelites moved on. *(They move toward paper river.)* At the Jordan, the priests picked up the ark and entered the water. *(Priests step to water's edge.)* As soon as they did, the water stopped flowing and piled up in a heap. *(Someone rolls up paper river.)* All the Israelites crossed on dry ground. Then the priests with the ark stepped across to the other side and the water flowed back in place. *(Priests move toward Jericho side.)*

Chorus: *(Sing "The Israelites Crossed the Jordan," page 20.)*

Israelite 1: *(Pointing)* Look! The walls of Jericho are shut up tightly!

Israelite 2: They must know we crossed the river, and they must be afraid.

Joshua: The Lord has revealed a plan to me. Jericho will soon fall.

Israelite 3: What is the plan?

Joshua: We will march around Jericho once a day for six days. The armed guard will lead. Next will come seven priests carrying trumpets of rams' horns in front of the ark of the covenant. The rear guard will follow.

Israelite 4: I will get the people lined up for our first day's march. *(Gets everyone in line—armed guard, priests, those with ark, rear guard.)*

Army: *(Characters sing appropriate verses of "Marching Israelites," page 16, as they march around the wall.)*

Narrator: And so they marched once around the city the first six days.

Army: *(Characters sing "The First Six Days," page 20, as they march.)*

Joshua: Today we will march around the city seven times. The seventh time around, when the priests sound a long trumpet blast, everyone will shout, and the walls of Jericho will tumble down.

Army: *(Sing "Great Jericho's Walls," page 20. At appropriate times, priests blow trumpets, Israelites shout, and someone behind wall knocks it down.)*

Joshua: *(Sings "Jericho is Falling Down," page 20, and everyone charges wall.)*

Chorus: *(Sings "Joshua's Army," page 20.)*

Joshua: The Lord has given you the city! *(Falls down as others rush off stage. He takes off robe and beard to signify he's schoolboy waking up. Rubs head.)* Where am I?

Tyler: *(Returning with Joshua's dad)* In Kansas, of course!

Joshua: *(Rubs head)* But I was just in Jericho.

Dad: Come on, Son. Let's get you to a doctor to check that lump on your head. *(Dad and two boys exit.)*

Shining Star, Copyright © 1995

0-382-30643-0

Songs Sung New

Are the Spies Still Here?
Tune: "Do Your Ears Hang Low?"

Are the spies still here?
Are they hidden somewhere near?
Are they hidden in the front?
Are they hidden in the rear?
Can you tell us what you know?
Can you guess where they would go?
Are the spies still here?

Rahab Let the Spies Climb Down
Tune: "London Bridge"

Rahab let the spies climb down,
Spies climb down, spies climb down.
Rahab let the spies climb down,
Helpful lady.

The Israelites Crossed the Jordan
Tune: "The Bear Went Over the Mountain"

The Israelites crossed the Jordan.
The Israelites crossed the Jordan.
The Israelites crossed the Jordan.
And they did it on dry ground.

Great Jericho's Walls
Tune: "The Mulberry Bush"

Here we go 'round great Jericho's walls,
Great Jericho's walls, great Jericho's walls
Here we go 'round great Jericho's walls
So early in the morning.

This is the way the long blast sounds…

This is the way we give a shout…

This is the way the walls fall down…

Jericho Is Falling Down
Tune: "London Bridge"

Jericho is falling down,
Falling down, falling down.
Jericho is falling down.
Charge in. Take it!

Joshua's Army
Tune: "Humpty Dumpty"

Joshua's army circled the wall.
When they all shouted, the wall took a fall.
Joshua, the leader, and all his armed men
Ran toward the city and charged right in.

The First Six Days
Tune: "Over in the Meadow"

Over on the plains when up came the sun
Rose an army and its leader,
Joshua, son of Nun.
"March," said the Lord.
"We'll march and have fun."
And they marched 'round the city
On day number one.

Over on the plains when the day dawned new
Rose an army and its leader,
While Jericho's fears grew.
"March," said the Lord.
"That's just what we'll do."
And they marched 'round the city
On day number two.

Over on the plains when the daylight broke free
Rose an army and its leader
Who knew just what was to be.
"March," said the Lord.
"We'll march, you will see."
And they marched 'round the city
On day number three.

Over on the plains in the Bible days of yore
Rose an army and its leader
Who prepared for a war.
"March," said the Lord.
"We'll march as before."
And they marched 'round the city
On day number four.

Over on the plains as the sun rose in the sky
Rose an army and its leader
Whose camp came alive.
"March," said the Lord.
"We'll march," they replied.
And they marched 'round the city
On day number five.

Over on the plains as the sun's colors mixed
Rose an army and its leader
Who had Jericho in a fix.
"March," said the Lord.
"We'll march just for kicks."
And they marched 'round the city
On day number six.

Over on the plains as the sun lit the heavens
Rose an army and its leader
And trumpeting priests seven.
"March," said the Lord.
"We'll march times seven."
And they marched 'round the city
On day number seven.

0-382-30643-0

At the End of the Rope

Preparation: Mount this page and page 22 on heavy paper that can't be seen through and cut out all the cards.

Directions: Two or three players may play this game. Shuffle all the cards and deal five to each player. Put the remaining cards facedown in a stack. The player with the highest double goes first by laying the double down faceup. (If no player was dealt a double, reshuffle and deal again.) The next player adds to the rope by putting down a card with the same number of knots on either rope end. Players take turns adding to the rope. When a player cannot add to the rope with a card in his hand, he must draw from the stack until he gets a card that may be added to the rope. The first player to get rid of all his cards is the winner. If all cards have been drawn from the pile and no player can add to the rope, the player with the least number of cards left in his hand is the winner.

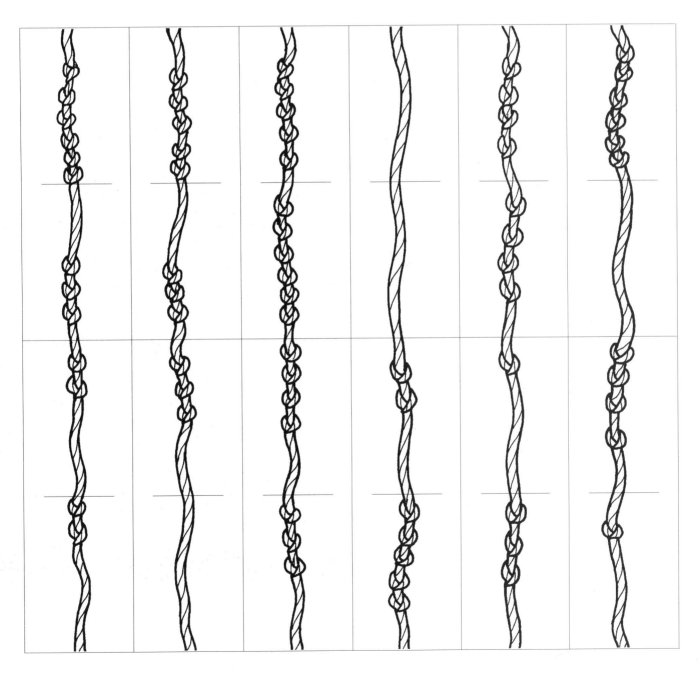

0-382-30643-0

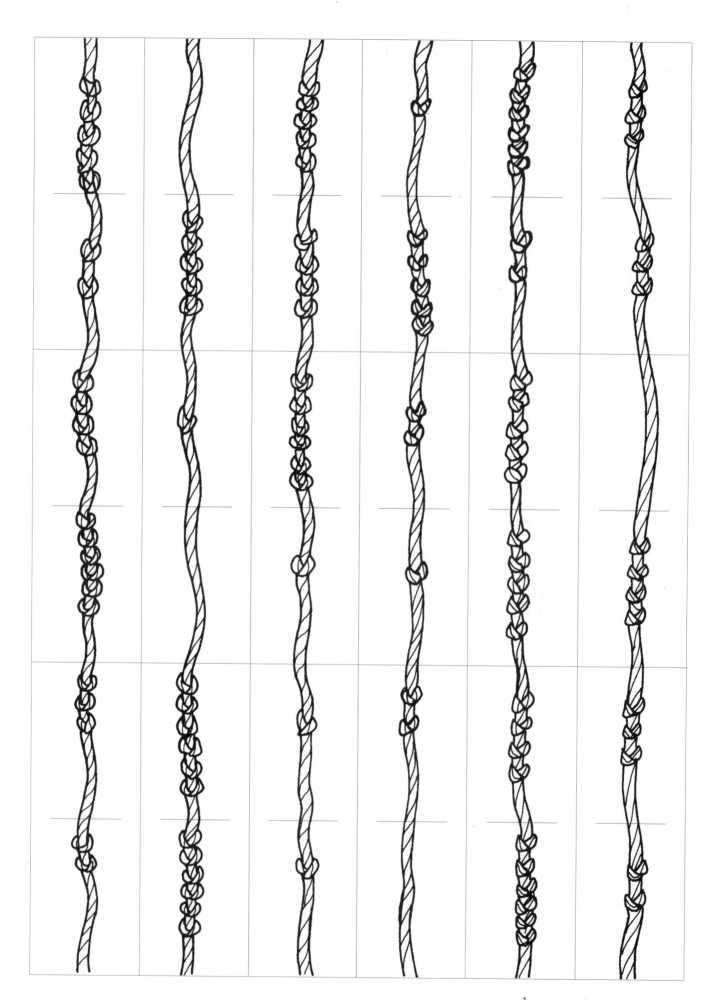

0-382-30643-0

Joshua Art Projects

Decorate a room with these projects and invite others to your Bible hero art "museum."

Twelve Stones

After the people crossed the Jordan River, Joshua had some men take twelve stones from the river—one for each tribe. As a group project, get twelve smooth stones. Then find out the names of the twelve tribes of Israel and paint the stones with those names.

Build a Wall

Build the walls of Jericho out of blocks, sugar cubes, etc. Add tiny paper figures to your scene. You may want to build the walls of Jericho as a class project, using large boxes and adding life-sized paper figures to the scene.

Wall-to-Wall Scenes

Choose a part of Joshua's story to illustrate. Hang your drawing close to your classmates' drawings to form a wall-like shape.

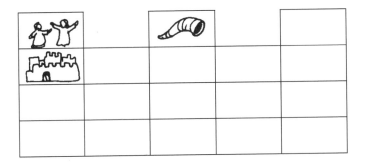

The Ark

Imagine what the ark of the covenant might have looked like. Decorate a box with bric-a-brac, cord, pasta shapes, or ancient drawings to represent the ark.

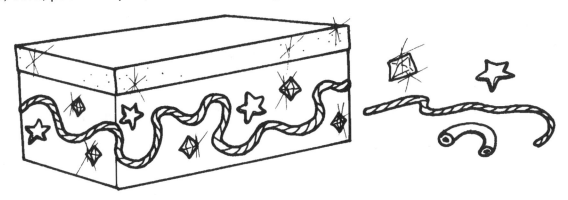

0-382-30643-0

The Story of Gideon

A Story Based on Judges 6-7

(Note: Use the patterns on pages 25, 35, 36, 39, and 43 to create flannel board pieces, stick puppets, or play props to emphasize the underlined words of the story.)

Long ago, under an oak tree, the angel of the Lord appeared to a man named Gideon. Gideon was threshing wheat, hiding from the Midianites, who had invaded the land and were ruining the crops of the Israelites. "The Lord is with you, mighty warrior," the angel said to Gideon. Gideon was astonished to learn that the Lord wanted him to save the Israelites from the Midianites. How could he, Gideon, save Israel? He could not believe his eyes and ears. He wanted a sign that he had found favor with the Lord. So, Gideon went to get an offering. He prepared goat meat and made some bread. Then he took the food to the angel, who told Gideon to put it on a rock. The angel touched the food with his staff. Fire burned up the food and the angel disappeared. It had truly been the angel of the Lord!

That night, the Lord told Gideon to tear down the altar to Baal and build in its place a new one to the Lord. Gideon took ten of his servants and did as the Lord said. The next day, the men of the town demanded that Gideon be put to death. His father convinced them not to kill Gideon. He said, "If Baal is really a god, he can defend himself when someone breaks down his altar."

Not long afterwards, the Spirit of the Lord came upon Gideon, and he assembled an army. Gideon asked God for a special sign. "If you are really going to use me to save the Israelites, let the fleece I put on the ground be covered with dew, but let the ground around it be dry." The next day, everything was just as Gideon had asked. Still, Gideon wanted another sign. He asked that the fleece be dry and the ground be wet. God did just what Gideon asked.

The next day God said to Gideon, "Your army is too large. If you use so many men, the Israelites may not think I helped deliver them from the Midianites. Let the frightened ones leave." Gideon did, and 22,000 men left. "There are still too many," the Lord said. "Take them to the water to drink and I will separate them there." When the men got a drink, the Lord told Gideon to keep only those who lapped the water like a dog. Only 300 men were left to fight the Midianites, who were as thick as locusts in the land and impossible to count!

God knew Gideon was afraid to attack with so few men. During the night, He sent Gideon and his servant to the edge of the Midianite camp to hear what they were saying. Gideon heard a man interpreting a dream about a barley loaf that knocked over the Midianite camp. He was told it was Gideon defeating the Midianites. When Gideon heard the meaning of the dream, he went back to the Israelite camp and told his army to get ready. He gave each man a trumpet and a jar with a torch under it. Then he divided the men into three groups and they surrounded the Midianite camp. They blew their trumpets, broke their jars, held up their torches and shouted, "A sword for the Lord and for Gideon!"

When the trumpets sounded, the Lord caused the Midianites to run and to turn on each other with their swords. With Gideon and just 300 men, the Lord's deliverance of the Israelites from the Midianites had begun.

0-382-30643-0

Celebrating the Bible Hero, Gideon

Gideon Galore

1. Publish a newspaper entitled the *Gideon Gazette*, featuring stories of events in Judges 6-7.

2. Create a Gideon Gallery of art projects. The gallery could include mobiles made from the patterns on page 43, drawings of events in Judges 6-7, clay jars, and tissue paper torches.

3. Have a Gideon Game Day. To play "Midianite Mash," roll socks into round "barley loaves" and use them to knock over miniature paper bag tents. To play "Wet Fleece," soak two towels with water and let contestants try to be the first to fill a bowl with water squeezed from a towel. Have a Gideon Grab Bag filled with slips of paper marked *kneeler*. Add a few pieces of paper that say *lapper*. A player who reaches into the bag and chooses a paper marked *lapper* wins.

4. Use the patterns on this page and pages 35, 36, 39, and 43 to create pencil toppers for a job well done, or add them to the top of a heavy strip of paper to create biblical bookmarks. Use them as prizes on Gideon Game Day.

5. Use the certificate above as an invitation to your Gideon Gallery, Gideon Game Day, or play. Use it as an award for a great performance, as a reward for completion of the Gideon activity sheets, as a take-home memory verse card, or as a thank-you note.

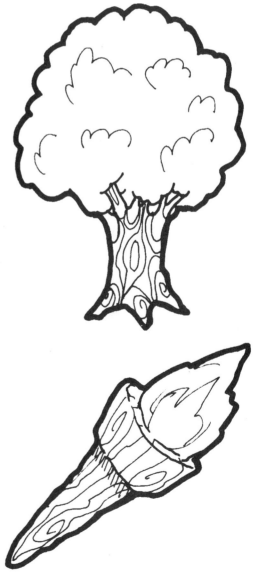

0-382-30643-0

A New Altar

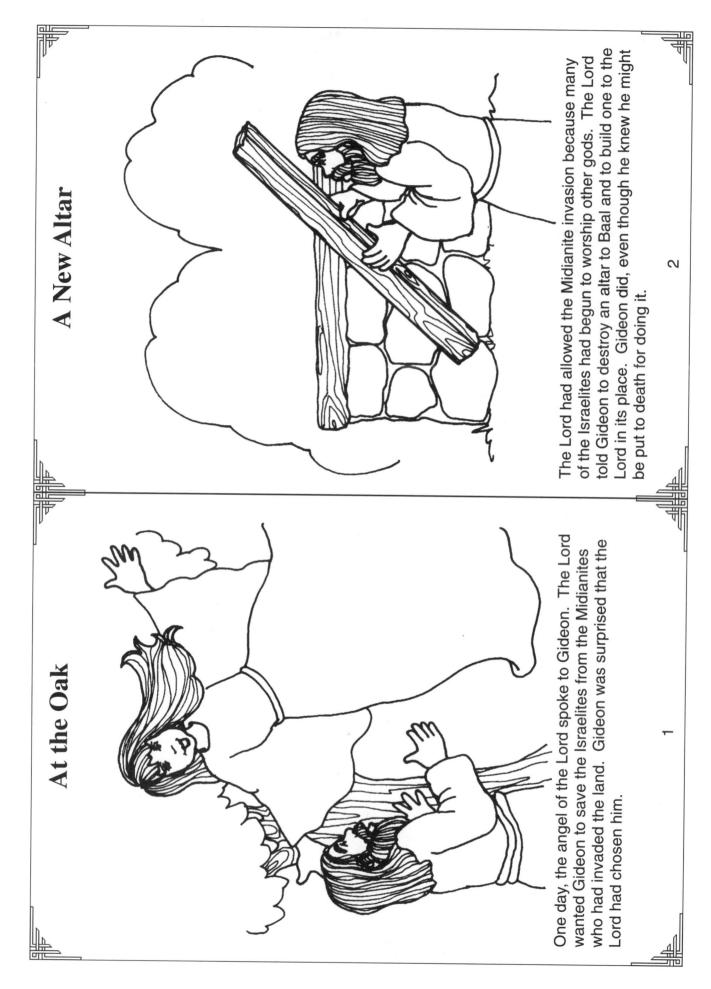

The Lord had allowed the Midianite invasion because many of the Israelites had begun to worship other gods. The Lord told Gideon to destroy an altar to Baal and to build one to the Lord in its place. Gideon did, even though he knew he might be put to death for doing it.

2

At the Oak

One day, the angel of the Lord spoke to Gideon. The Lord wanted Gideon to save the Israelites from the Midianites who had invaded the land. Gideon was surprised that the Lord had chosen him.

1

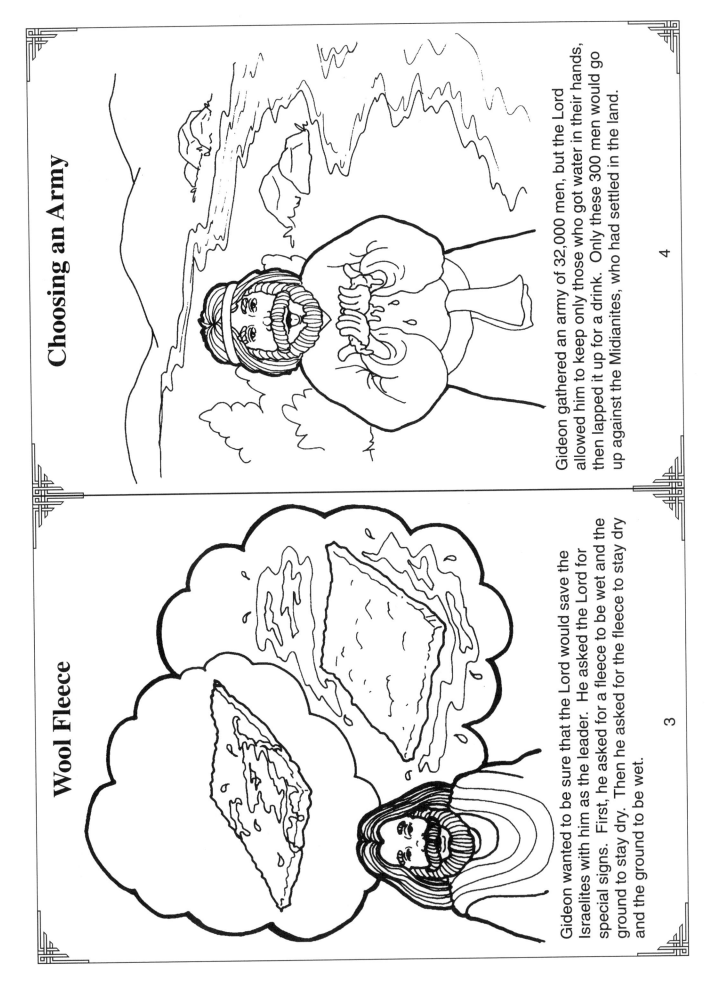

Choosing an Army

Gideon gathered an army of 32,000 men, but the Lord allowed him to keep only those who got water in their hands, then lapped it up for a drink. Only these 300 men would go up against the Midianites, who had settled in the land.

4

Wool Fleece

Gideon wanted to be sure that the Lord would save the Israelites with him as the leader. He asked the Lord for special signs. First, he asked for a fleece to be wet and the ground to stay dry. Then he asked for the fleece to stay dry and the ground to be wet.

3

0-382-30643-0

Trumpet Sounds

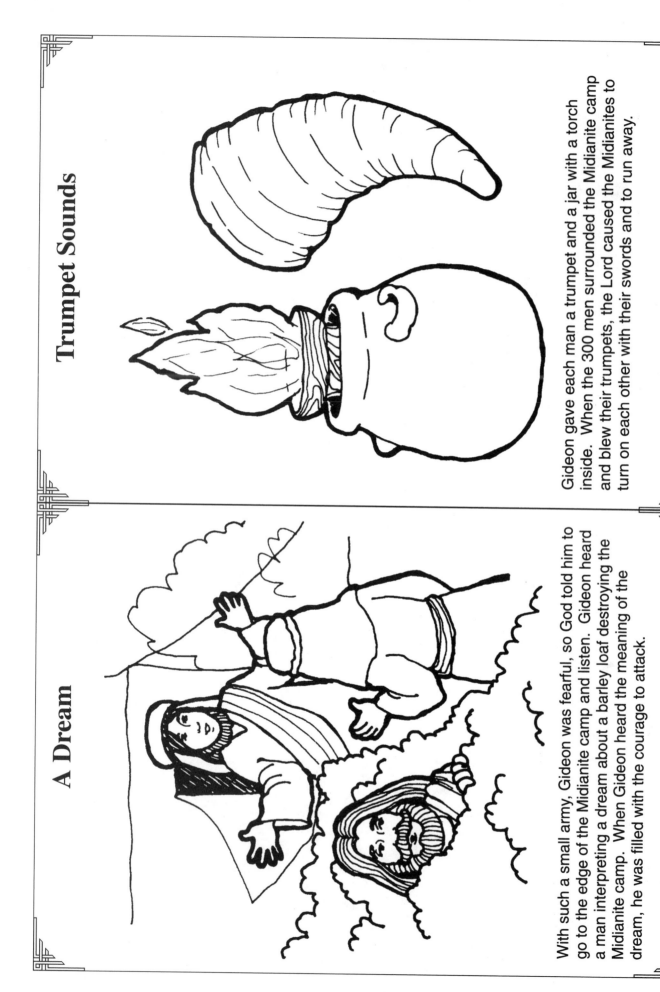

Gideon gave each man a trumpet and a jar with a torch inside. When the 300 men surrounded the Midianite camp and blew their trumpets, the Lord caused the Midianites to turn on each other with their swords and to run away.

6

A Dream

With such a small army, Gideon was fearful, so God told him to go to the edge of the Midianite camp and listen. Gideon heard a man interpreting a dream about a barley loaf destroying the Midianite camp. When Gideon heard the meaning of the dream, he was filled with the courage to attack.

5

0-382-30643-0

Under the Oak

Find and circle the given words.

```
G  I  D  O  N  P  O  D  P  B
C  G  R  L  E  G  N  A  P  G
B  O  I  D  G  C  K  D  B  I
C  A  P  D  E  A  R  A  R  D
B  T  P  A  E  R  B  E  O  E
G  O  A  B  A  O  E  R  G  O
T  B  A  S  K  E  T  B  T  N
```

GIDEON

ANGEL

BREAD

OAK

BASKET

POT

GOAT

"Gideon went in, prepared a young goat, and from an ephah of flour he made bread without yeast. Putting the meat in a basket and its broth in a pot, he brought them out and offered them to him under the oak."

Judges 6:19

0-382-30643-0

An Altar to the Lord

Gideon took ten of his servants with him to build an altar to the Lord. Draw lines to the matching pairs. Then color the matching ones alike.

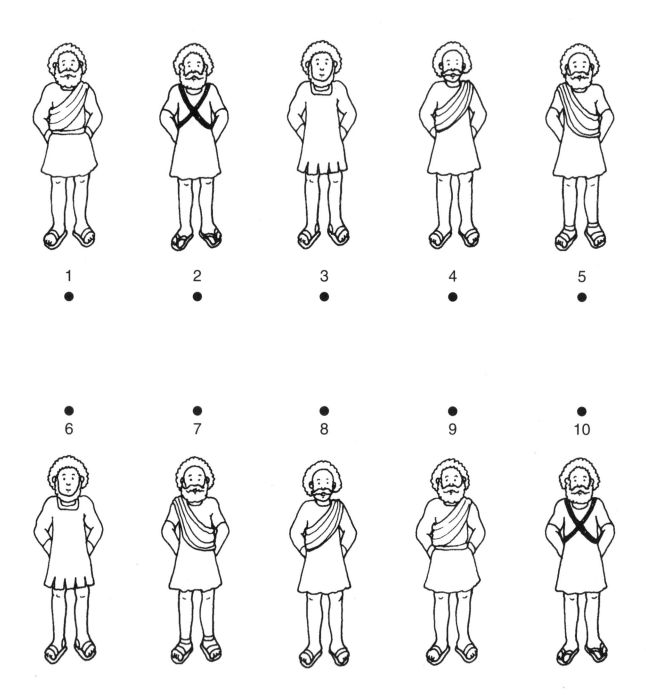

1   2   3   4   5

6   7   8   9   10

"…Tear down your father's altar to Baal and cut down the Asherah pole beside it. Then build a proper kind of altar to the Lord your God on the top of this height…."   Judges 6:25-26

Shining Star, Copyright © 1995

30

0-382-30643-0

A Special Sign for Gideon

Gideon wanted to be sure that God would save the Israelites with his help, so he asked God to give him a special sign. Fill in the matching letters for the symbols to find out what Gideon said to God.

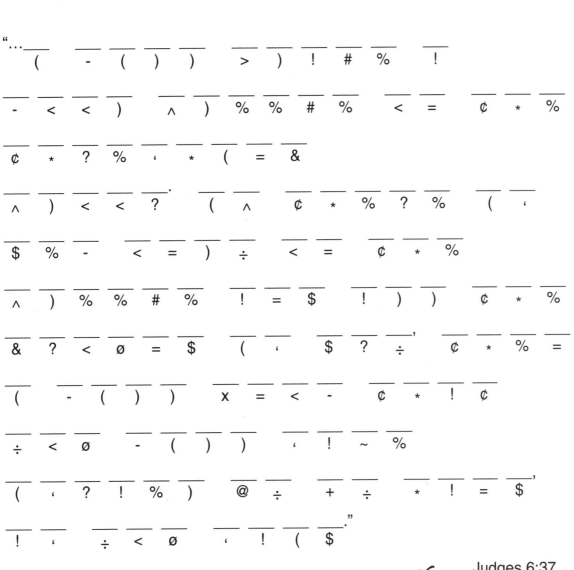

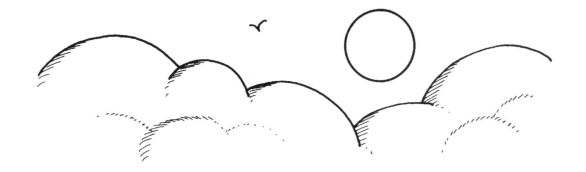

Judges 6:37

A	!
B	@
C	#
D	$
E	%
F	^
G	&
H	*
I	(
K	x
L	)
M	+
N	=
O	<
P	>
R	?
S	'
T	¢
U	ø
V	~
W	-
Y	÷

31

0-382-30643-0

A Small Army Remains

Fill in a letter to complete each word from Judges 7:5. Then use the words to tell how many men were left in Gideon's army. Write the completed words on the corresponding numbered lines at the bottom of the page.

1. ☐ O
2. W I T ☐
3. W A T E ☐
4. T H O S ☐
5. S E P A R A T ☐

6. W ☐ O
7. T O N G ☐ E S
8. K ☐ E E L
9. ☐ O G
10. T H E I ☐
11. T H ☐
12. ☐ O W N

13. F R O ☐
14. L I K ☐
15. D R I ☐ K

"..._____ _____ _____ lap _____
     5   4   6   11

_____ _____ _____ _____
     3   2   10   7

_____ a _____ _____ _____
    14   9   13   4

_____ _____ _____ _____
     6   8   12   1

_____."
    15

Judges 7:5

Barley Loaves

Gideon overheard a man interpreting a dream about a barley loaf that came tumbling into the Midianite camp. Find and circle ten loaves of barley bread hidden in the picture.

"Gideon arrived just as a man was telling a friend his dream. 'I had a dream,' he was saying. 'A round loaf of barley bread came tumbling into the Midianite camp. It struck the tent with such force that the tent overturned and collapsed.'" Judges 7:13

Broken Jars

Read or listen to Judges 7. Then draw lines to connect the broken pieces to form key words from Gideon's story. Write the words on the lines.

_____ _____ _____

_____ _____ _____

_____ _____ _____

"...They blew their trumpets and broke the jars that were in their hands."   Judges 7:19

0-382-30643-0

Gideon/Spy Mask

Color, cut out, and laminate the mask below. To make a face mask, punch a small hole on each side and add string or elastic. To make a stick mask, attach a paint stirring stick to the back. To make a puppet, attach the face to a paper bag. Use it when putting on a presentation about Gideon. (This pattern may also be used to represent a spy in the story of Joshua.)

0-382-30643-0

Gideon Finger Puppet Song

Color and cut out the figures below. Glue each one to a ring-sized paper band and use it when performing the song below. You may want to laminate the figures or back them with lightweight cardboard before cutting them out. Attach an ice-cream stick to the back of each one to make a stick puppet for a shoe box stage or back the figure with felt for use with a flannel board. The figures may also be enlarged to make paint-stick puppets.

TOO MANY MEN

FRIGHTENED ONES

Too Many Men in My Army
Tune: "Skip to My Lou"

Too many men, oh, what should I do?
Too many men, oh, what should I do?
Too many men, oh, what should I do?
Too many men in my army.

God says let the frightened ones go.
God says let the frightened ones go.
God says let the frightened ones go.
Too many men in my army.

Still thousands left, oh, what should I do?
Still thousands left, oh, what should I do?
Still thousands left, oh, what should I do?
Too many men in my army.

God will sift them by the water's edge.
God will sift them by the water's edge.
God will sift them by the water's edge.
Too many men in my army.

Most kneel to drink. God says, "Let them go."
Most kneel to drink. God says, "Let them go."
Most kneel to drink. God says, "Let them go."
Too many men in my army.

Three hundred left that lapped like a dog.
Three hundred left that lapped like a dog.
Three hundred left that lapped like a dog.
They'll make up my army.

WATER

DOG

KNEELING MAN

Shining Star, Copyright © 1995

0-382-30643-0

Once Upon a Bible Story
Under an Old Oak Tree

> Characters: Grandpa, Girl, Boy, Angel, Gideon, Chorus, Israelite Men, Servant, Midianites 1-5 and other Midianites
>
> Setting: A backdrop with an oak tree at the left and one at the center
>
> Props: Toy meat and bread, rock, staff, one wet and one dry piece of fleece or other material, cardboard swords, paper cone trumpets, clay or plastic jars, cardboard torches with tissue paper flames

Girl: *(Enters with Grandpa and Boy)* Grandpa, will you tell us a story?

Grandpa: Sure. *(Points to left tree)* Let's sit in the shade over there.

Boy: *(All three sit)* What kind of tree is this?

Grandpa: It's called an oak and it reminds me of a Bible story.

Girl: I hope it's about an angel.

Boy: I hope it's about a soldier.

Grandpa: Well, this story has something for both of you. *(Gideon enters and pretends to thresh wheat near center oak)* Once upon a Bible time, under an old oak tree, the angel of the Lord appeared to a man named Gideon. *(Angel enters with staff)*

Angel: The Lord is with you, mighty warrior.

Gideon: *(Looking up)* How can the Lord be with us? The Midianites are ruining our land and our lives. The Lord has abandoned us to them.

Angel: Go, and with your strength save Israel from the Midianites.

Chorus: *(Sings "By the Old Oak Tree," page 40.)*

Gideon: Me! How can I do it? My clan is the weakest and I am the least in my family. If I have really found favor with my Lord, give me a sign. ·

Grandpa: *(Gideon and angel do what Grandpa says)* Yes. He went off to prepare some meat and bread. When he returned, the angel told Gideon to put the meat and bread on a rock. The angel touched the food with his staff. Fire burned it up and the angel disappeared. *(Exits)*

Boy: Wow!

Grandpa: That night, the Lord told Gideon to tear down the altar to Baal and build a new one to the Lord in its place. Gideon did what the Lord asked. The next day, the men of the town told Gideon's father what had happened. They demanded that Gideon be brought out and put to death.

Chorus: *(Sings "An Altar," page 40.)*

0-382-30643-0

Grandpa: Gideon's father said to the men, "If Baal is really a god, he can defend himself." So the men left Gideon alone. Not long after that, Gideon began to gather together an army, but it still was hard for him to believe that God had chosen him to lead the Israelites. *(Gideon begins pacing with a piece of fleece in his hand as he looks upward.)*

Gideon: If You will really save Israel like You promised with me as the leader, give me a sign. Look. I will place this wool fleece on the ground. *(Lays fleece down)* In the morning, if there is dew on the fleece, but the ground is dry, then I know You will save Israel by my hand. *(Lies down to sleep)*

Chorus: *(Sings two verses of "Gideon's Requests," page 40. Gideon awakens at second verse, picks up wet fleece and squeezes water into a bowl.)*

Gideon: The fleece is wet and the ground is dry, but is it really a sign that God will save Israel by my hand? *(Paces, holding fleece again.)* God, please don't be angry with me, but let me make just one more test. This time, make the fleece dry and the ground covered with dew.

Chorus: *(Sings last two verses of "Gideon's Requests." On last verse, Gideon awakens and touches the fleece and the ground.)*

Grandpa: When Gideon woke up, the ground was wet and the fleece was dry. The next day, Gideon and the army he had assembled camped near a spring not far from the camp of the Midianites. *(Lots of men enter.)*

Girl: How many men did Gideon gather?

Grandpa: He gathered as many as he could—thirty-two thousand men—but God told him that was too many. The Israelites might brag that they had won with their own strength, not the help of God. So God told Gideon how to reduce the size of his army.

Gideon: *(Sings "Too Many Men in My Army," page 36, as men act out verses—some leaving scared, some drinking on knees, etc.)*

Grandpa: Gideon ended up with 300 men. *(Men lie down)*

Girl: Is 300 a lot?

Grandpa: Oh no! The Midianites had settled in the valley as thick as locusts, and their camels were as impossible to count as the grains of sand on the seashore!

Boy: Gideon must have been worried with so few men to fight so many.

Grandpa: He was, but God told him to go with his servant to the edge of the Midianite camp and listen to what they were saying. *(Gideon and another sneak near Midianites and cup hands to ears)*

Midianite 1: I had a dream of a round loaf of barley that rolled into the Midianite camp with such force that the tent overturned and fell down.

Midianite 2: The dream is about Gideon, the Israelite. It means that God will give the whole Midianite camp into his hands.

Gideon: *(Returns with servant to men)* Get up and get ready! The Lord will give the Midianite camp into our hands. We will divide into three companies. *(Divides men into three groups)* Everyone take a trumpet and jar with a torch inside. *(Everyone takes trumpet and jar with torch)* Each company will surround a different side of the Midianite camp. Follow my lead and do as I do. When we blow our trumpets, the rest of you blow yours too, and shout. *(Three companies split and quietly surround Midianites)*

Grandpa: When Gideon and those with him reached the edge of the camp, they blew their trumpets and broke their jars. *(Those with Gideon blow trumpets and drop jars to reveal torches)* Then the other groups did the same. *(Rest of men act this out)* With their torches in their left hands, they shouted.

Israelites: A sword for the Lord and for Gideon!

Midianite 3: What's going on?

Midianite 4: The Israelites have surrounded us. We must fight!

Midianite 5: No! We must run!

Grandpa: When the trumpets sounded, the Midianites were confused and the Lord caused them to turn on each other with their swords and to run away.

Israelites: *(Sing "We're in Gideon's Army," page 40, as Midianites flee)*

Grandpa: Then Gideon called on more men to go after the Midianites and to capture their leaders. So, Gideon, with God's help, saved the Israelites.

Boy: That was a good story.

Girl: And to think… it all started under an oak, like this one.

Chorus: *(Sing "Choosing an Army," page 40.)*

ANGEL   FLEECE

                                    0-382-30643-0

Songs Sung New

By the Old Oak Tree
Tune: "Kookaburra"

Gideon worked by the old oak tree,
Threshing wheat where Midian wouldn't see.
Work, Gideon. Work, Gideon.
Hard your life must be.

An angel spoke by the old oak tree.
"Mighty warrior, the Lord's with thee."
Go, Gideon. Go, Gideon.
A leader you must be.

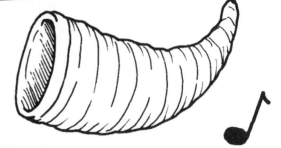

We're in Gideon's Army
Tune: "I'm a Little Teapot"

We're in Gideon's army, small but grand.
We have trumpets and jars in hand.
When we give a shout and take a stand,
Our enemies all leave the land.

Choosing an Army
Tune: "Pop Goes the Weasel"

Gideon sent his messengers out
To gather an army of many.
Thirty-two thousand came but God said,
"No! That's too many."

Gideon sent the fearful ones back.
The numbers that left were many.
Ten thousand stayed but still the Lord said,
"No! That's too many."

Gideon watched the man get a drink.
Down on their knees went many.
Three hundred lapped like a dog and God said,
"Three hundred's plenty!"

Gideon's Requests
Tune: "This Old Man"

Lord, if with hands of mine
You'll save Israel, give this sign:
Make the ground of the threshing floor
Stay all dry and yet
Make the fleece upon it wet.

Gideon, the next day
Saw God sent a sign his way.
The ground of the threshing floor
Was all dry and yet
The fleece on the ground was dripping wet.

Lord, I pray I'm not out of line.
Give me yet another sign.
Make the fleece on the threshing floor
Stay all dry and yet
Make the ground around it wet.

Gideon, the next day,
Saw God sent a sign his way.
The fleece on the threshing floor
Was all dry and yet
The ground around the fleece was wet.

An Altar
Tune: "Ate a Peanut"

Downed an altar, downed an altar,
Downed an altar last night.
Last night, Gideon downed an altar,
Downed an altar built to Baal.

Built a new one, built a new one.
Built a new one last night.
Last night, Gideon built a new one,
Built a new one to the Lord.

0-382-30643-0

300 Men Game

Preparation: Mount this page and page 42 on thick paper and cut out all the cards.

Directions: Two to four players may play this game. The object of the game is to get a total of 300 men by getting one each of the following cards: 40, 50, 60, 70, and 80. Shuffle all the cards and place them facedown in rows. Players take turns choosing a card or putting one back. The first player to have a total of 300 men is the winner.

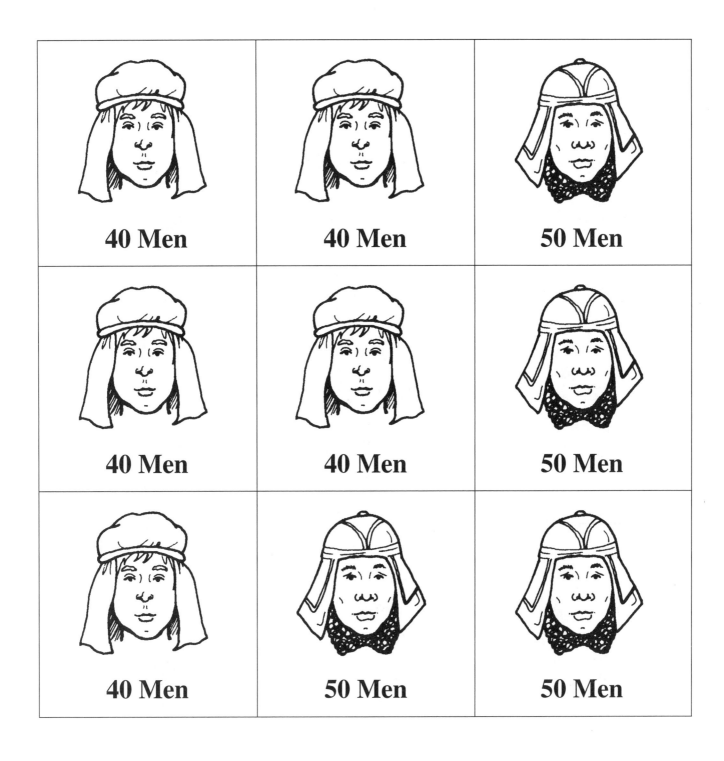

40 Men   40 Men   50 Men

40 Men   40 Men   50 Men

40 Men   50 Men   50 Men

0-382-30643-0

Game Cards

0-382-30643-0

Gideon Mobile

Color the figures below. Mount the page on thick paper and cut out each figure. Write a verse from the story of Gideon on the back of each one. Punch a hole near the top of each one and add yarn or string. Attach the figures to a hanger or another object to form a mobile.

TORCH

TRUMPET

GIDEON

CLAY JAR

SWORD

0-382-30643-0

The Story of Ruth

A Story Based on Ruth 1-4

(Note: Use the patterns on pages 15, 45, 55, 58-59 to create flannel board pieces, stick puppets, or play props to emphasize the underlined words of the story.)

Long ago, when judges led Israel, there was a famine in the land. A man named Elimelech, his wife, Naomi, and their two sons left Bethlehem and went to live in Moab. Elimelech died there and Naomi was left with her two sons. The two sons married women of Moab. One of the women was named Orpah and the other was named Ruth. Several years later, both of Naomi's sons died.

When Naomi heard that there was food once again in Bethlehem, she decided to go home. Naomi and her daughters-in-law set out on the road that would lead them to Bethlehem. Along the way, Naomi said to them, "Go back, each of you, to your mothers' houses. May the Lord be kind to you as you have been to me." Orpah kissed Naomi good-bye and turned back. Ruth, though, clung to Naomi.

When Naomi tried again to convince her to leave, Ruth said, "Don't tell me to leave. Where you go, I will go. Your people will be my people and your God will be my god." So the two women went together. They arrived in Bethlehem just as the barley harvest was beginning.

"Let me go into the fields and pick leftover barley behind anyone who will let me," Ruth said to Naomi. She went to work in a field, stopping only a short time to rest. When Boaz, the owner of the field, saw Ruth, he asked the head of the harvesters about her. Then he spoke to Ruth and told her to stay near his servant girls and to work only in his field where she would be safe. He also told her to get a drink from the water jars whenever she wanted one. Ruth bowed before him and asked, "Why are you treating me, a foreigner, with such kindness?"

Boaz answered, "I've been told what you have done for Naomi. May the Lord reward you for your loyalty." Boaz offered Ruth some food, and when she went back to work, Boaz told the harvesters to leave some extra handfuls of barley behind for her to pick up. When Ruth showed Naomi all she had gathered, Naomi was amazed and asked where she had worked. Then she told Ruth that Boaz was a kinsman-redeemer, a relative of her dead husband.

One day, Naomi sent Ruth to Boaz. She wanted to know if he would marry Ruth and buy the land that had been owned by Naomi's husband and sons, since he was a kinsman-redeemer. Boaz told Ruth there was a closer relative that had to be given the chance to buy the land first.

Boaz went to the town gate and sat there until the other kinsman-redeemer came along. In front of ten elders of the town, Boaz told the other man about the land Naomi wished to sell and about Ruth. The other man did not want to redeem the land, so he told Boaz to do it. Then the man took off his sandal and gave it to Boaz as a sign that the transfer of the land was final. Thus, Boaz acquired the land and married Ruth. They had a son and named him Obed. Naomi helped to care for him and he brought her joy. And the women of the town told Naomi she was fortunate to have a loyal daughter-in-law such as Ruth.

Celebrating the Bible Hero, Ruth

Remembering Ruth

1. After talking about Ruth 4:7, give each child several paper sandals on which to write promises he will keep or chores he will perform for others. Children may display the sandals on a bulletin board or give them as gifts.

2. Have a Ruth Race. See who can "glean" the most litter from the playground or lunchroom.

3. Have a Ruth reception after presenting the play on page 60. Serve foods made with barley and wheat.

4. Plan Ruth's wedding to Boaz. Where will the ceremony be? Who will be included on the guest list? What food will be served? What entertainment will there be? Who will perform the ceremony? What will Ruth's dress and ring look like?

5. Use the certificate/bookmark above as an invitation to a play, an award for a great performance, a reward for completion of the Ruth activity sheets, a take-home memory verse card, or a thank-you note.

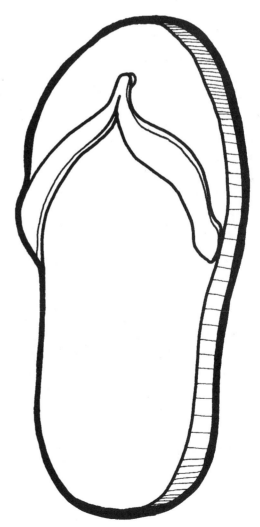

0-382-30643-0

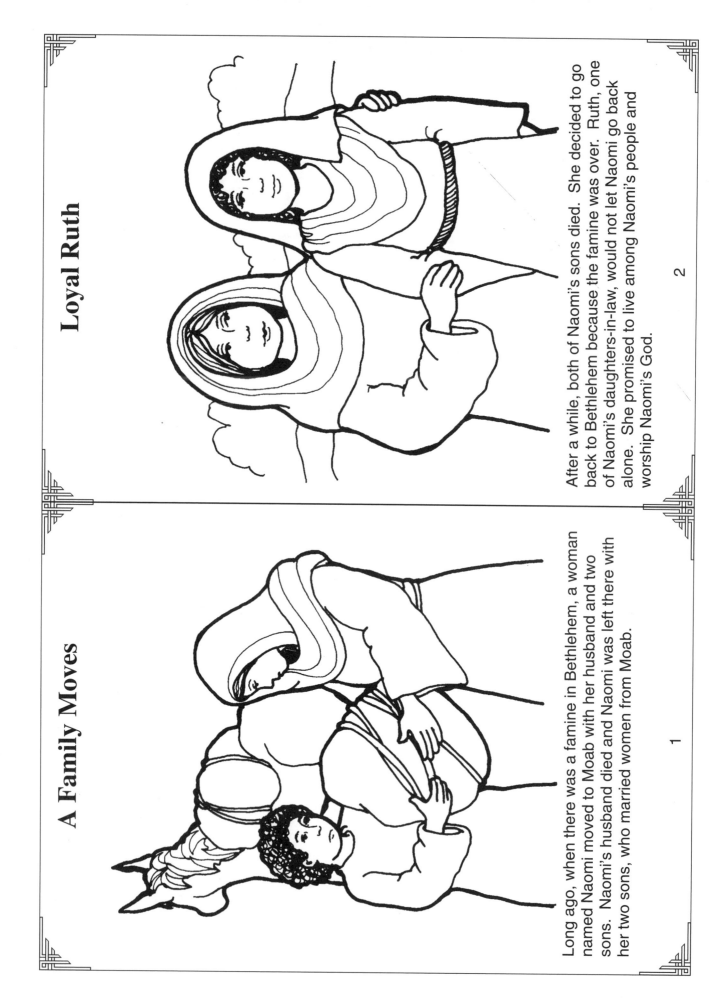

Loyal Ruth

After a while, both of Naomi's sons died. She decided to go back to Bethlehem because the famine was over. Ruth, one of Naomi's daughters-in-law, would not let Naomi go back alone. She promised to live among Naomi's people and worship Naomi's God.

2

A Family Moves

Long ago, when there was a famine in Bethlehem, a woman named Naomi moved to Moab with her husband and two sons. Naomi's husband died and Naomi was left there with her two sons, who married women from Moab.

1

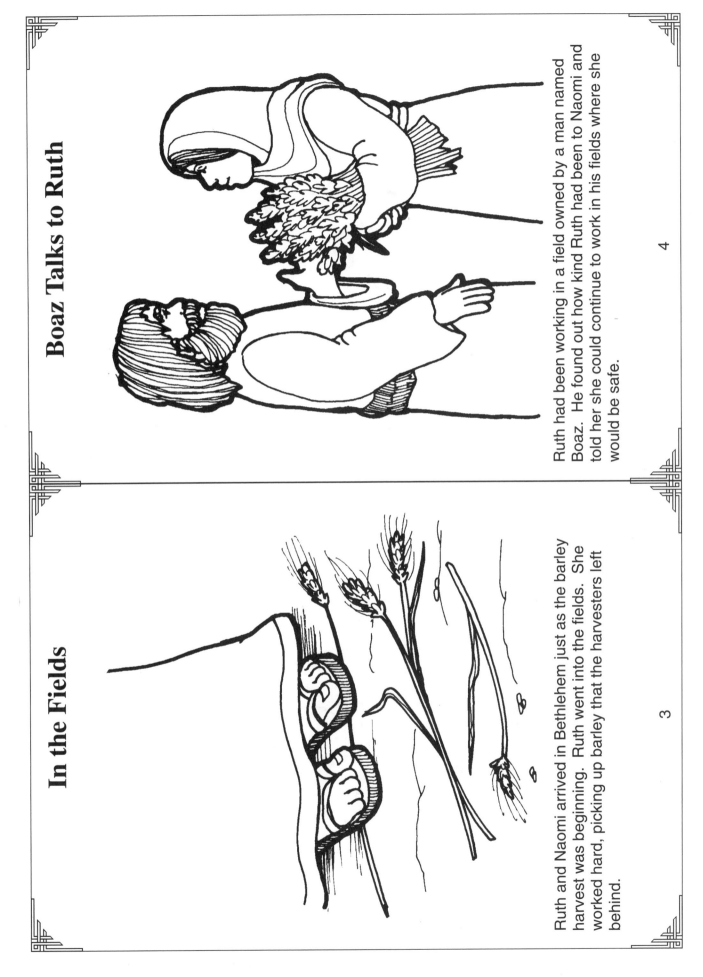

Boaz Talks to Ruth

Ruth had been working in a field owned by a man named Boaz. He found out how kind Ruth had been to Naomi and told her she could continue to work in his fields where she would be safe.

4

In the Fields

Ruth and Naomi arrived in Bethlehem just as the barley harvest was beginning. Ruth went into the fields. She worked hard, picking up barley that the harvesters left behind.

3

47

0-382-30643-0

Boaz Marries Ruth

Boaz bought the land that had belonged to Naomi's husband and sons. In doing so, he also acquired Ruth as his wife. Boaz and Ruth had a son, whom they named Obed. The child was a blessing to Naomi, who helped care for him.

6

Ruth Shares

Ruth continued to work hard in the field. She threshed the barley she gathered and shared it with her mother-in-law, Naomi. All through the barley and wheat harvests, Ruth worked only in the field belonging to Boaz.

5

Shining Star, Copyright © 1995

0-382-30643-0

Naomi Goes to Moab

Help Naomi and her family get from Bethlehem to Moab.

MOAB

"In the days when the judges ruled, there was a famine in the land, and a man from Bethlehem in Judah, together with his wife and two sons, went to live for a while in the country of Moab."

Ruth 1:1

Ruth and Naomi

Solve the puzzle by switching each letter for its partner.

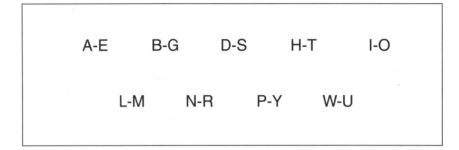

A-E   B-G   D-S   H-T   I-O

L-M   N-R   P-Y   W-U

"... U T A N A   P I W   B I O   U O M M

B I   E R S   U T A N A   P I W   D H E P

O   U O M M   D H E P .   P I W N

Y A I Y M A   U O M M   G A L P

Y A I Y M A   E R S   P I W N   B I S

L P   B I S ."

Ruth 1:16

0-382-30643-0

Leftovers

Cross out each J, Q, X, and Z in the puzzle below. Write the leftover letters in order on the lines to complete the Bible verse.

```
Q  J  Z  Q  X  L  E  X  T  M  E  J  G  O  T
O  T  H  X  E  F  I  E  Z  L  D  J  S  A  N
J  D  P  I  Z  C  K  Z  U  P  J  T  J  H  E
Z  L  E  Q  X  F  T  J  O  Z  V  X  Q  J  E
R  G  R  J  A  I  N  B  E  H  X  I  N  D  A
N  Y  O  J  N  E  I  N  W  H  O  Q  S  E  E
X  Y  E  S  I  F  I  N  D  F  A  Q  V  O  R
```

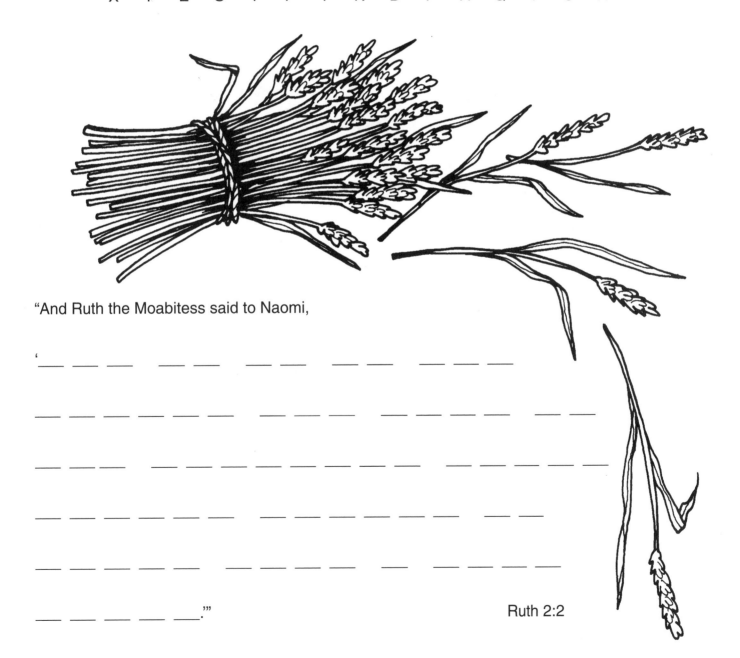

"And Ruth the Moabitess said to Naomi,

'___ ___ ___ ___ ___ ___ ___ ___ ___ ___

___ ___ ___ ___ ___ ___ ___ ___ ___ ___

___ ___ ___ ___ ___ ___ ___ ___ ___ ___

___ ___ ___ ___ ___ ___ ___ ___ ___ ___

___ ___ ___ ___ ___.'"

Ruth 2:2

0-382-30643-0

A Kind Man

To find out the name of the man who treated Ruth kindly, color each space containing a word from the verse below.

"Her mother-in-law asked her, 'Where did you glean today? Where did you work? Blessed be the man who took notice of you!'"

Ruth 2:19

0-382-30643-0

Finding Grain

Find and circle ten heads of grain hidden in the picture below.

"So Ruth stayed close to the servant girls of Boaz to glean until the barley and wheat harvests were finished. And she lived with her mother-in-law."

Ruth 2:23

0-382-30643-0

At the Gate

Find and circle the seven words from Ruth's story in the puzzle.

```
G   A   T   S   A   N   D   L   P
A   L   R   R   E   T   A   G   P
L   O   A   E   G   N   O   M   I
C   A   B   D   E   A   R   M   R
B   T   O   L   N   R   O   R   B
D   O   Z   E   A   A   E   U   O
T   N   A   S   N   E   S   H   A
A   B   A   H   T   U   R   T   Z
L   A   N   L   A   T   B   O   A
```

RUTH   BOAZ   NAOMI   ELDERS

LAND   GATE   SANDAL

"Then Boaz announced to the elders and all the people, 'Today you are witnesses that I have bought from Naomi all the property of Elimelech, Kilion and Mahlon. I have also acquired Ruth the Moabitess, Mahlon's widow, as my wife....'"

Ruth 4:9-10

0-382-30643-0

Ruth/Rahab Mask

Color, cut out, and laminate the mask below. To make a face mask, punch a small hole on each side and add string or elastic. To make a stick mask, attach a paint-stirring stick to the back. To make a puppet, attach the mask to a paper bag. Use the mask when putting on a presentation about Ruth. (This pattern may also represent Rahab in the story of Joshua.)

0-382-30643-0

Naomi and Ruth Game

Color the game board on this page and page 57 and tape them together. Two to four players may play this game. Each player will need a marker, such as a colored paper clip or a button to place on START. Players take turns rolling a die and moving the number of spaces indicated by the die. Players must follow the directions on the spaces on which they land. The first player to reach FINISH (an exact count is not needed) is the winner.

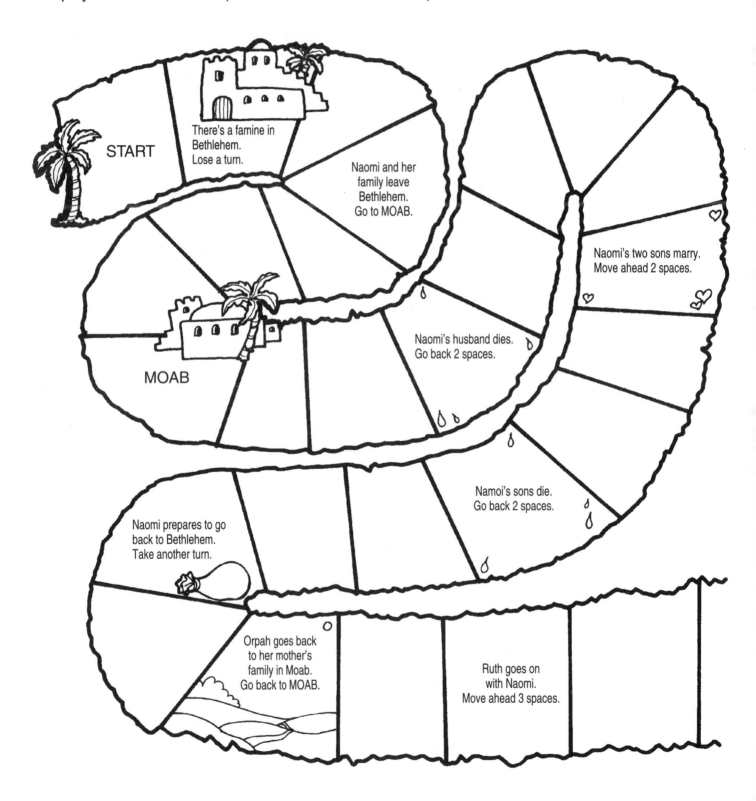

START

There's a famine in Bethlehem. Lose a turn.

Naomi and her family leave Bethlehem. Go to MOAB.

Naomi's two sons marry. Move ahead 2 spaces.

MOAB

Naomi's husband dies. Go back 2 spaces.

Namoi's sons die. Go back 2 spaces.

Naomi prepares to go back to Bethlehem. Take another turn.

Orpah goes back to her mother's family in Moab. Go back to MOAB.

Ruth goes on with Naomi. Move ahead 3 spaces.

0-382-30643-0

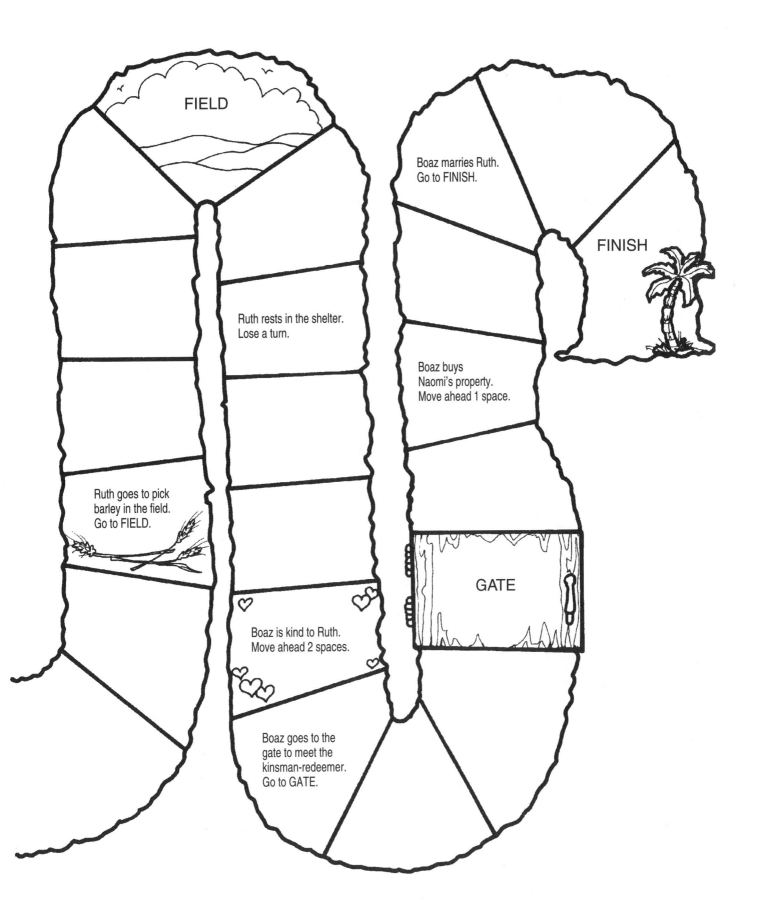

FIELD

Ruth rests in the shelter.
Lose a turn.

Ruth goes to pick
barley in the field.
Go to FIELD.

Boaz is kind to Ruth.
Move ahead 2 spaces.

Boaz goes to the
gate to meet the
kinsman-redeemer.
Go to GATE.

Boaz marries Ruth.
Go to FINISH.

FINISH

Boaz buys
Naomi's property.
Move ahead 1 space.

GATE

0-382-30643-0

Naomi Finger Puppet Song

Color and cut out the figures below. Glue each one to a ring-sized paper band and use it when performing the song below. You may want to laminate the figures or back them with lightweight cardboard before cutting them out. Add an ice-cream stick to the back of each one to make a stick puppet for a shoe box stage or back the figures with felt for use with a flannel board. The figures may also be enlarged to make paint stick puppets.

NAOMI

RUTH

HUSBAND

Naomi's Song
Tune: "The Farmer in the Dell"

Naomi took a husband.
Naomi took a husband.
Long ago in Bible times,
Naomi took a husband.

Then they had two sons…

The family left their home…

They went to live in Moab…

One son married Ruth…

The sons and husband died…

Naomi left for home…

Ruth stayed by her side…

Naomi wasn't alone…

SON

SON

Ruth Bible Story Patterns

Reduce or enlarge these figures and the ones on page 58 for puppets, flannel board stories, bulletin board displays, shoe box dioramas, shoe box stages, stationery, pencil toppers, storytelling, play props or backgrounds.

BETHLEHEM

BARLEY

FIELD/LAND

ORPAH

BOAZ

OBED

Naomi and Ruth
A Story of Loyalty

Characters: Narrator(s), Orpah, Ruth, Naomi, Chorus, Boaz, Head Harvester and other Harvesters, Elders, Kinsman wearing sandals.

Setting: A backdrop with a gate painted on one side and a field on the other side with grain nearby on the ground.

Props: Grain

Narrator: Long ago, when judges led Israel, there was a famine in the land. A man named Elimelech took his wife, Naomi, and their two sons to live in Moab. The man died and Naomi was left with her two sons. Both sons married women of Moab. Years later, both sons also died. Naomi was left only with her two daughters-in-law, Orpah and Ruth.

Naomi: Orpah and Ruth, I have learned that there is food now in my home land. I have decided to return there to be with my people.

Orpah and Ruth: We will come with you.

Narrator: The three of them set out toward the land of Judah.

Naomi: Both of you, go back to your mothers. *(Sings "Naomi's Advice," page 62.)*

Narrator: Orpah and Ruth cried, but Orpah finally kissed her mother-in-law good-bye and turned back. Ruth, though, clung to Naomi.

Naomi: Orpah is going back to her people. You go too, Ruth.

Ruth: No. I want to go where you go and stay where you stay. Your people will be my people and your God will be my God.

Ruth and Chorus: *(Sing "I Won't Leave You," page 62.)*

Narrator: Naomi and Ruth went together. *(Walk on)* They arrived in Bethlehem just as the barley harvest was beginning. *(Harvesters enter)*

Ruth: Let me go into the fields and pick leftover grain behind anyone who will let me.

Naomi: Go ahead, my child. *(Ruth goes to field and begins to follow along after harvesters. She picks grain off ground. Boaz enters.)*

Boaz: The Lord be with you, harvesters.

Harvesters: The Lord bless you.

Boaz: *(Takes head harvester aside)* Who is that young woman?

Head Harvester: She is the woman that came from Moab with Naomi. She has worked steadily all morning except for a short rest in the shelter.

Boaz: *(Approaches Ruth)* My child, don't go to work in anyone else's field. Stay and work near my servant girls and you will be safe.

Chorus: *(Sing "Ruth's Been Workin'," page 62.)*

Shining Star, Copyright © 1995

0-382-30643-0

Ruth: *(Kneels at his feet)* Why are you treating me, a foreigner, so kindly? *(Harvesters sit down and begin to eat.)*

Boaz: I have heard all you have done for Naomi. May the God of Israel reward you for what you have done. Here, have some roasted grain. *(Ruth sits and eats, then goes back to picking leftover grain. Boaz speaks to sitting harvesters.)* Even if she gathers among the sheaves, don't stop her, and let some extra grain fall for her to pick up.

Narrator: Ruth stayed in the field until evening. *(Harvesters exit and Ruth walks to Naomi's house.)* Then she threshed the barley she had gathered and showed Naomi how much there was.

Naomi: Where did you work? Blessed be the man who took notice of you.

Narrator: Ruth told Naomi all that had happened. She continued to work in Boaz' fields throughout the harvest. One day, Naomi sent Ruth to Boaz.

Naomi: Boaz is a kinsman-redeemer. He can marry you and provide for you. Go to him to see if he will help.

Narrator: Boaz told Ruth that he wanted to help, but there was a closer relative that must be asked first. Boaz went to the town gate and waited with the elders for the other kinsman to come along. *(Boaz sits at gate with elders. Kinsman comes along and Boaz motions him to sit down.)*

Boaz: Naomi is selling the land that belonged to our brother. If you will redeem it, do so. If not, I will, for I am next in line.

Kinsman: I will do it.

Boaz: If you do, you also acquire Ruth as a wife, in order to maintain the name of the dead with the property.

Kinsman: Then I cannot do it. That would endanger my own estate. Here, take my sandal as a sign that I am transferring the property to you. *(Removes a sandal and gives it to Boaz.)*

Boaz: You are all witnesses. Today, I have bought Naomi's land and acquired Ruth as my wife.

Chorus: *(Sing "A Kinsman-Redeemer," page 62.)*

Narrator: So Ruth and Boaz got married.

Chorus: *(Sing "Ruth is Marrying Boaz," page 62.)*

Narrator: Ruth and Boaz had a son. They named him Obed. His birth brought Naomi joy and she helped to care for him. Obed became the father of Jesse who became the father of David. *(All sing "Loyal Ruth," page 62.)*

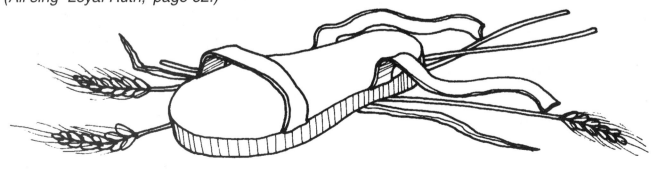

Shining Star, Copyright © 1995

0-382-30643-0

Songs Sung New

Naomi's Advice
Tune: "Go Tell Aunt Rhodie"

Listen, Ruth and Orpah,
Listen, Ruth and Orpah,
Listen, Ruth and Orpah,
I'm going back to my home.

Go back to your mothers,
Go back to your mothers,
Go back to your mothers,
And I'll go on alone.

I Won't Leave You
Tune: "My Bonnie Lies Over the Ocean"

Your people will be my people.
Your God will be my God, too.
Where you die, there I will be buried.
Oh, please let me stay with you.

I won't leave you.
Oh, I won't leave you alone, alone.
I won't leave you.
I'll go with you to your old home.

Ruth's Been Workin'
Tune: "I've Been Workin' on the Railroad"

Ruth's been workin' in the fields-oh
All the livelong day.
Ruth's been workin' in the fields-oh
Pickin' grain all day.
Can't you see how hard she's workin'—
Gleaning the barley?
Can't you see how hard she's workin'—
Gath'ring 'mong the sheaves?

Boaz says, "Don't go." Boaz says, "Don't go."
Boaz says, "Don't go to another's land."
Boaz says, "Don't go." Boaz says, "Don't go.
Stay here upon my land."

A Kinsman-Redeemer
Tune: "For He's a Jolly Good Fellow"

Boaz is a kinsman-redeemer.
Boaz is a kinsman-redeemer.
Boaz is a kinsman-redeemer,
So he can marry Ruth.

Ruth is Marrying Boaz
Tune: "Sally's Wearing a Red Dress"

Ruth is marrying Boaz, Boaz, Boaz.
Ruth is marrying Boaz. Sing a song!

Ruth is marrying Boaz, Boaz, Boaz.
Ruth is marrying Boaz. Ding, ding, dong!

Loyal Ruth
Tune: "Old King Cole"

Loyal Ruth was a loving young soul.
A loving young soul was she.
She clung to Naomi,
Her mother-in-law.
Great was her loyalty.

0-382-30643-0

Answer Key

Going to Jericho, Page 9

"Then Joshua son of Nun secretly sent two spies from Shittim. 'Go look over the land,' he said, 'especially Jericho.'"

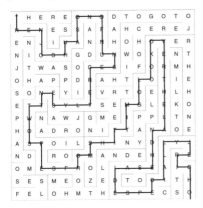

Spies in Hiding, Page 10

"(But she had taken them up to the roof and hidden them under the stalks of flax she had laid out on the roof.)"

On Dry Ground, Page 11

Seven Priests with Seven Trumpets, Page 12

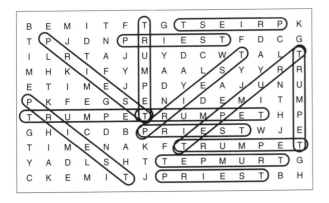

Seven Times Around, Page 13

"The seventh time around, when the priests sounded the trumpet blast, Joshua commanded the people, 'Shout! For the Lord has given you the city!'"

Tumbled Wall Jumble, Page 14

trumpets, people, sound, loud, shout, wall, collapsed, charged, straight, city

Under the Oak, Page 29

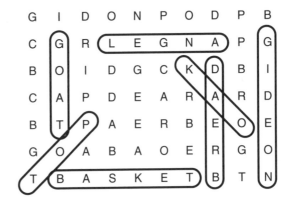

An Altar to the Lord, Page 30

2 and 10, 1 and 9, 3 and 6, 4 and 8, 5 and 7

A Special Sign for Gideon, Page 31

"…I will place a wool fleece on the threshing floor. If there is dew only on the fleece and all the ground is dry, then I will know that you will save Israel by my hand, as you said."

A Small Army Remains, Page 32

THREE HUNDRED MEN

"…Separate those who lap the water with their tongues like a dog from those who kneel down to drink."

   0-382-30643-0

Answer Key

Barley Loaves, Page 33

Broken Jars, Page 34
jars, hundred, camp, hands, Midian, Gideon, sword, trumpets, torches

Naomi Goes to Moab, Page 49

Ruth and Naomi, Page 50
"…Where you go I will go, and where you stay I will stay. Your people will be my people and your God my God."

Leftovers, Page 51
"…Let me go to the fields and pick up the leftover grain behind anyone in whose eyes I find favor."

A Kind Man, Page 52

Finding Grain, Page 53

At the Gate, Page 54

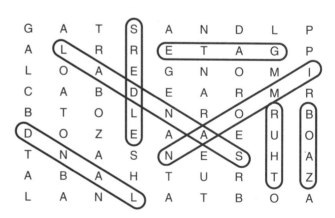

Shining Star, Copyright © 1995

0-382-30643-0